Cam and Pat

by Liza Charlesworth

ISBN: 978-1-338-84425-2

Art Director: Tannaz Fassihi; Designer: Cynthia Ng; Illustrated by Kevin Zimmer
Copyright © Liza Charlesworth. All rights reserved. Published by Scholastic Inc.

3 4 5 6 7   68   26 25 24

Printed in Jiaxing, China. First printing, June 2022.

Cam is a ram.
Cam is at the top
of a big hill.

Pat is a rat.
Pat is NOT at the top
of a big hill.

Pat did miss his pal
Cam A LOT!
But Pat did not get sad.

Pat got his bag.
Pat got his map.
Then Pat got in a cab.

CAB

5

But the cab got stuck
in a lot of mud.

Pat did not get sad.
Pat got on a bus.

But the bus had
ten men on it.
Pat did not fit!

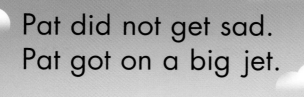

Pat did not get sad.
Pat got on a big jet.

FAB RAT JETS

MAP

The jet went
up, up, up, up, up!

FAB RAT JETS

Did Pat jump?
Yes, Pat did!

11

"It is Pat!" said Cam.
"It is Cam!" said Pat.

Then the rat and ram
did a big jig.
Hip, hop, hip, hop!

Read & Review

Invite your learner to point to each short-vowel word and read it aloud.

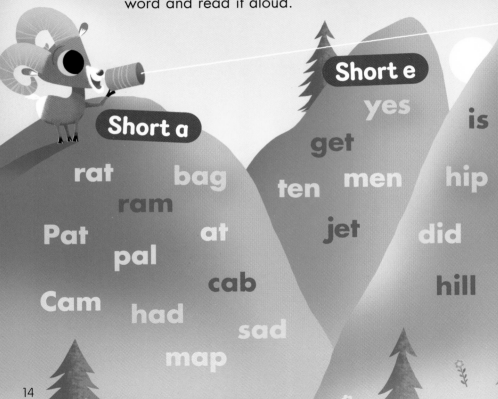

Short a

rat
bag
ram
Pat
at
pal
cab
Cam
had
sad
map

Short e

yes
get
ten
men
jet

is
hip
did
hill

Short i

his

in

big

fit

miss

it

jig

Short o

top

not

on

lot

got

hop

Short u

but

mud

bus

up

stuck

jump

Fun Fill-Ins

Read the sentences aloud, inviting your learner to complete them using the short-vowel words in the box.

> jig   lot   mud   ram   jet

1. Pat is a rat, and Cam is a _____.
2. Pat wanted to see Cam a _____!
3. Pat's cab got stuck in _____.
4. To get to Cam, Pat flew in

   a _____.
5. At the end, Cam and

   Pat did a big _____.